Grandma's 25 Cent Words

Making Good Values the Foundation of a Child's Education and Life

JUDITH MARTIN ALFORD

ReadersMagnet, LLC

DEDICATED

WITH MUCH LOVE AND
THANKFULNESS

TO

THE FATHER, THE SON,
AND THE HOLY SPIRIT

TABLE OF CONTENTS

FOREWORD

The creation of this book has been an unusual experience from its first conception. I was in prayer when I heard God say to me, "Write down these words: Integrity, courageous, respectful, humbleness, honesty, obedience..." He gave me a very long list. He continued to say: "These values are missing in most of our children today and in the lives of many adults. Write a children's book about them." So here is its completion!

I thank God for guiding me and for giving me many of the ideas for "Grandma's 25 Cent Words." The story about Grandma's word bank is true. I have dyslexia and I am still a slow reader! When this book was about half completed, God woke me in the middle of the night. He told me to write down the rest of the book's title. I wrote down: "Making Good Values the Foundation of a Child's Education and Life."

It is my sincerest hope and desire that this small book will lead this once great nation back to God, our Father. It is time once again that all of us will listen to one another, especially when our opinions differ. Good manners and listening to two sides of the story leads us out of our individual grey areas and gets us closer to God's truth!

God, our Father has entrusted all the adults of today with loving, teaching, and caring for all our children and youth. My prayer is that He will guide each and everyone of us to do an outstanding job. I know with His help we can be better than we have ever been before in teaching them that God is the Truth, the Light and the only Way. May God bless us all in this endeavor.

Amen.

Dear Parents and Teachers,

The lessons and activities in this book were designed for elementary children with the hopes that Junior High and High School youth would help in teaching each lesson. Younger children always look up to those a little older than themselves. The youth helping out in the teaching will become great role models.

Each chapter begins with a Medal of Honor. In the center of the coin medal is the word highlighted in the chapter. This is meant to be colored by the child either at the beginning or the end of that lesson.

Each activity highlights a career emphasis that child might be interested in pursuing in their life. Children learn by playing and it is fun watching their talents develop!

I am hopeful that this book will be used in home schooling, Sunday School classes, and youth groups. The lessons were not planned to go in the exact order that they are presented in this book. If as a parent or teacher, you feel one of the values need to be taught sooner, jump ahead to teaching it. You may also want to review some lessons you already taught. Values are not taught in just one lesson. A child's maturation level can make a big difference.

Each child develops at their own rate of growth so some of the values may needed to be taught later or in several lessons. Have fun moving at their pace and remembering sometimes to challenge them too!

God bless all of you,
P.J. Alford

The Pledge of Allegiance to the United States of America[1]

I Pledge allegiance, to the flag,
of the United States of America.
And to the republic, for which it stands,
one nation under God
indivisible, with liberty
and justice for all.

Grandma's Favorite Story

Hello!

You can just call me Grandma. If your Grandma lives far away from you or if you don't have a Grandma, well now you do! I have short, white, curly hair that looks like a fuzzy teddy bear! I am chubby and love to give big hugs. I smile a lot and I love to tell stories. Would you like to hear a story today?

A very long time ago, when I was little and learning how to read, I found some words very difficult to understand. They may have had many meanings or had been hard to spell. Some of them were even tough to say!

My Mom and my Dad would say to me, "Why that is just a **25 Cent Word!**"

A 25 Cent Word....well, that meant that I had better learn it! They were really telling me that it was valuable. It was a word that I should learn about and put in my big, imaginary, but very useful word bank!

Learning a new **25 Cent Word** also meant to me that I had to make that word become a part of me. I had to learn to live it! This was not always easy!

When I was little, I could buy a whole loaf of bread for only 25 cents! My parents could get one gallon of gasoline or buy a quart of milk for just 25 cents. I got paid 25 cents an hour for my first baby sitting job. In those days 25 cents was a lot of money. Plus, four 25 cent coins made a whole dollar. I thought I was very rich when I had a dollar!

In time, I found that money was not as important as a **25 Cent Word.** Words are powerful. Words can express our feelings when we are happy or sad. Words can help us get things we need like a toy we can't reach in our closet or directions to go to see Grandma when we are lost. Words help us tell time, make a friend, or purchase a new pair of shoes. Words can tell a story. I love to read. I love to draw and I love to write. Do you?

Play a game with me today!

I am going to share with you my favorite **25 Cent Words** in this book but first you will need a Word Bank to put them into to keep them forever.

So please draw a picture of what your word bank looks like on the bottom of this page. What does it look like? Will you draw a dinosaur word bank, a teapot word bank, or a piggy word bank? I can't wait to see what it looks like and what color you will make it. Don't forget to draw a picture of your new Grandma next to it.

I will be giving you lots of **25 Cent Words** to put in your word bank so you will grow up to be a very kind, intelligent person. Your new Grandma will be so proud of you and I bet all the people in your family will be too!

IV. ACTIVITY: **Being an Artist!**

Directions: Draw a picture of yourself with your new Grandma. Draw a picture of what your WORD Bank looks like. Don't forget to color it!

CHAPTER 1

INTEGRITY

Color this medal once you have learned this word!

INTEGRITY

I.   Say: Integrity: In teg' ri tee

II.   Meaning: Doing what is right even if no one is looking!

III.   Bible Verse: Luke 6:31 tells us to "Do to others as you would have them do to you." (NIV)

I like people to be kind to me so, I should be kind to them first.

Be kind to your Mom and Dad, to your brothers and sisters, to your teachers, and to people you want to be your friends.

When you have integrity, you are kind to people and they will trust you because they see integrity in all you do.

IV.   Situation: A big shaggy dog with long ears and big brown eyes shows up at your home! He is lost. He has a collar on but no tags. You really want to keep him. He would be lots of fun. What would you do?

V.   Solution: I would show **I have integrity** in this situation by:

1.

2.

3.

4.

VI. ACTIVITY: **Being a Cartoon Artist!**

Directions: Draw a cartoon here about your shaggy dog **integrity** story.

Name of my cartoon is: _____

Artist Illustrator: Sign your work here:_____

CHAPTER 2

COURAGEOUS

Color this medal once you have learned this word!

COURAGEOUS

I.   Say: Courageous   Kur' age us

II.   Meaning: To be brave, bold, daring, strong hearted, to show valor

III.   Bible Verse: Deuteronomy 31:6 says: "Be strong and courageous. Do not be afraid or terrified because of them, for the Lord your God goes with you; He will never leave nor forsake you." (NIV)

IV.   Situation: You are ice skating on a pond with a group of your friends. No grownups are near you. Your brother falls through the ice.

        What would you do to save your brother and to show you are courageous?

        Remember the ice around your brother is very thin and you do not want anyone else to fall through the ice.

V.   Solution: I would show **I am courageous** in this situation by:

        1.

        2.

        3.

        4.

VI. ACTIVITY: **Being a Poet!**

Write a poem or a rap about being courageous. I will start one for you or you can do one on your own.

Courageous is a mighty word.

CHAPTER 3

Color this medal once you have learned this word!

RESPECTFUL

I.   Say: Respect: Ree speck' ful

II.   Meaning: To honor and admire another person

III.   Bible Verse: 1Peter 2:17 " Show proper respect to everyone, love the family of believers," (NIV)

IV.   Situation: Your teacher has invited a guest into your classroom to share her job as a fireman. The lady fireman is wearing her uniform that she wears when she fights a fire.

V.   Solution: I will show **I have respect** for our classroom guest by:

1.

2.

3.

4.

VI. ACTIVITY: **Being A Word Picture Artist!**

Drawing a Word Picture.

1. Draw a picture of Grandma and you listening to a fireman at a fire.

2. Draw a big fire truck with hoses and a ladder on it.

3. Put words into your picture of what the fireman has asked you to do.

4. Show that because you respect the fireman and know she is trained to help, you will do what she asks.

5. Use word bubbles like this one ………...

CHAPTER 4

HUMBLENESS

Color this medal once you have learned this word!

HUMBLENESS

I.   Say: Humbleness: Hum' bull ness

II. Meaning: Having an unassuming, modest behavior, attitude, or spirit

III. Bible Verse: 1Peter 5:5 "…you who are younger, submit yourselves to your elders. All of you, clothe yourselves with humility toward one another, because, God opposes the proud but shows favor to the humble." (NIV)

IV. Situation: Your _____ team (You pick the sport) has just won the championship game. You are the captain of the team and you are about to be interviewed on TV. What should you say to show yourself as being humble?

V.   Solution: Write down some of your ideas to say in this interview to show you have a spirit of humbleness. Grandma will do one for you.

1. *My sport is a team sport. It takes more than just me to win.*

2.

3.

4.

VI. ACTIVITY: **Being a Writer!**

Write a short newspaper or magazine article about the humbleness, the captain of this team, has shown and how others admire him.

Title & Picture
Humble Writer   Sign your name here:

Draw an interesting picture along with the title of your article in the top space:

CHAPTER 5

Color this medal once you have learned this word!

HONESTY

I.   Say: Honesty: On' es tee

II. Meaning: To be truthful, trustworthy, fair, and good

III. Bible Verse: Ephesians 4:25 "Therefore each of you must put off
                    falsehood, and speak truthfully to your neighbor…" (NIV)

IV. Situation: Your best friend lives next door and she has a dog named Freddy.
     Your other neighbor has a dog named Max. One morning your Dad is not
     happy because he found a big hole in the ground next to his favorite rose
     bush. He thinks Max may have done it but you saw Freddy dig that hole.
     What should you do?

V.   Solution: I am an honest person so I would:

     1.

     2.

     This problem could best be solved by:

     3.

     4.

VI. ACTIVITY: **Being TV Reporters!**

Pretend that you are a reporter for a TV channel. Interview some members in your family or friends of yours. Ask them to tell you about a time in their life where they showed honesty. Grandma will tell you a story that happened to her.

Grandma's story

I went into a gift shop one day and tried on some winter gloves. When I tried on one pair, I felt a bump in one of the fingers. I wiggled my finger and found a ring! It was a diamond ring! I wanted to keep it but I told the clerk about my discovery. She put it in a safe and in time they found the lady that had lost it. She sent me a gift to thank me.

_____'s story about honesty:

_____'s story about honesty:

_____'s story about honesty:

CHAPTER 6

Color this medal once you have learned this word!

OBEDIENCE

I.   Say: Obedience: Oh bee' dee ence

II.   Meaning: Being willing to carry out the wishes of another person

III.   Bible Verse: Ephesians 6:1 "Children, obey your parents in the LORD, for this is right." (NIV)

IV.   Situation: Your Mom has asked you to clean your room today. Since you want to be obedient, you decide to clean up your room.

V.   Solution: Write down how your mother will feel when she sees your clean room and she realizes you were obedient to her wishes. Grandma did the first one for you.

1. *She will be proud of you for being obedient.*

2. She will be: _____

3. She will be: _____

4. She will be: _____

VI. ACTIVITY: **Being Portrait Artists!**

Play a game with me and **see how easy it is to be obedient:**

#1 Your teacher asks the class to stop talking.

SO, I WILL: _____

#2 Your Dad needs your help and asks you to take out the garbage.

SO, I WILL: _____

#3 Your Mom asks you to fasten your seat belt in the car

SO, I WILL: _____

Draw three faces of how these people will look when **you are obedient** to do what they ask of you!

CHAPTER 7

KINDNESS

Color this medal once you have learned this word!

KINDNESS

I.   Say: Kindness: Kind ' ness

II. Meaning: To be friendly, generous, or warm hearted in nature

III. Bible Verse: Proverb 16:24 "Kind words are like honey- sweet to the soul and healthy for the body." (NIV paraphrased for children)

IV. Situation: A new family has moved into your neighborhood this week. They have a boy who is 7 and a girl who is 4 years old. What could you do to make them feel welcomed and to show them kindness?

    See what Grandma's favorite thing is to do to welcome new people! Below my idea, write down three ideas you have **to be kind to them**.

V.   Solution:

1. Grandma would bake a batch of cookies to give to them.

2. I would: _____

3. I would: _____

4. I would: _____

VI. ACTIVITY: **Being Bakery Chefs!**

With a grown up, bake a batch of their favorite cookies or make them a cake! Maybe you would like to try one of Grandma's favorite recipes. Here is one of my favorites.

Monkey-Faced Cookies

Set Oven to 375 F.
Makes 4 dozen 2 1/2" Cookies

Mix together: ½ cup shortening
                  1 cup brown sugar
                  ½ cup molasses

Stir in: ½ cup sour milk
                  1tsp cider vinegar

Sift together and then stir into your mixture:

                  2 ½ cups flour
                  1 tsp. baking soda
                  ½ tsp. salt
                  ½ tsp. ginger
                  ½ tsp. cinnamon

Drop rounded teaspoons of dough 2 ½ inches apart on an ungreased cookie sheet
Place 3 raisins on each cookie for the eyes and mouth.
Bake 375 F. for 10 – 12 minutes
Cool 1 minute before removing cookies from the cookie sheet.
The monkey faces will take on droll expressions while baking. They will make you chuckle. I hope your new friends will like them too!

My Love to you, Grandma XOXOXO

CHAPTER 8

Color this medal once you have learned this word!

PATIENCE

I.   Say: Patience   pay′ ss hence

II.   Meaning: To remain calm even when you have to wait a long time.

III.   Bible Verse: Romans 8:25 "But if we hope for what we do not yet have, we wait for it patiently." (NIV)

IV.   Situation: You want a dirt bike but you must **be patient** while you save up the money to purchase it. What could you do to remain patient during this time period? You already know that it will not help you if you get angry or upset that it is taking such a long time to earn the money.

V.   Solution: I could remain patient during this time period by:

1. I could have fun riding my old bike.

2. I could: _____

3. I could: _____

4. I could: _____

VI. Activity: **Drawing Stick Figure Cartoons!**

Sometimes in life we have to be patient while we wait for our turn.

We might have to wait in a long line at the grocery store for our turn to get our groceries checked out.

Today, we are going to have fun drawing a stick figure cartoon!

Our picture story is about the time we went to the dentist and had to wait a long time before it was our turn to get our teeth checked.

Show yourself as not being patient at the beginning of your LONG wait but something happened that made your attitude change and you became calm and patient.

When you were told it was your turn to see the dentist you had a big smile on your face even though your front two teeth were missing!

This is what a stick figure looks like:

Here is my Stick Figure Cartoon:

Artist, please sign your name here:_____

CHAPTER 9

GENTLENESS

Color this medal once you have learned this word!

GENTLENESS

I.   Say: Gentleness: Gen' tle ness

II.   Meaning: Being kind, considerate, mild mannered, soft-hearted

III.   Bible Verse: Ephesians 4:2   "Be completely humble and **gentle;** be patient, bearing with one another in love." (NIV)

IV.   Situation: Proverbs 15:1 says: "A gentle answer turns away wrath (violence), But a harsh word stirs up anger."

Therefore, what would you do in this situation to calm down a fight you see brewing between two of your friends?

They are both in the front of a line at an amusement park to ride the roller coaster but only one seat is available. They both want to take that last seat so they start to shout and argue with one another.

How would your help them, using gentleness, to solve their problem? Grandma will give you one idea then you think up another one.

V.   Solution:

   1. Grandma: *"I would remind them **by not shouting** at them that we are all friends."*

   2. My idea is:

VI. ACTIVITY: Being an Investigator!

Today, we are going to go outside to a park, to a playground or even just watch how our brother or sisters play together at home. Our job is to investigate to see how many people are showing that they have a spirit of gentleness in them.

Fill in what you saw and what things a gentle person did in the chart below. Grandma did the first one to show you what she saw.

What I saw was:	Gentleness was shown by:
1. **Grandma saw this happen:** A girl fell down and started to cry.	**Grandma said:** "Her Dad picked her up and hugged her. He spoke with a very kind voice."
2. I saw this happen:	Tell what the gentle person did here:
3. I saw this happen:	Tell what the gentle person did here:

CHAPTER 10

SELF-CONTROL

Color this medal once you have learned this word!

SELF-CONTROL

I.   Say: Self-Control   Self- Con' trol

II.   Meaning: To be well behaved and to hurt no one

III.   Bible Verse: Galatians 5:23 "...gentleness, and **self- control**; Against such things, there is no law." (NIV)

IV.   Situation: Grandma is going to tell you 4 different stories. You are to put a check in front of the stories that showed you used self-control.[2]

V.   Solution: I am an honest person so I would:

     1. ____ You resisted doing something you knew was wrong.

     2. ____ You grabbed a toy you wanted off of a shelf in the store without asking a parent if you could have it.

     3. ____ You did not eat another cookie when you were already full.

     4. ____ When your teacher asked the class a question, you shouted the answer without raising your hand.

(Answers are on the bottom of the next page.)

VI. ACTIVITY: **Having Fun!**

The Game of <u>Pick Up</u>!

The number of people playing can be from 2 – 6 players

Directions:

    1. Give each person playing a bag and have them find and collect:

        One Penny

        One Pencil

        One Piece of Hard Candy (wrapped in paper)

        One Rubber band

        One Paper Clip

        One Small Stone (all about the same size)

        One Tall Plastic Cup

    2. Have each person sit down at a table where they have all of the same group of different items in front of them.

    3. **Say: Ready, Get Set, Go!**

    4. The object of the game is to see who can put all of their items into their plastic cup first. When s/he has it done, they shout: **"Done!"**

    5. Oh dear, Grandma forgot to tell you that you can only use One Hand's **FOUR FINGERS BUT NO THUMB !**

    6. This game takes great **SELF-CONTROL** to use only one hand and NO thumb!

Answers to page #23: Both #1and #3 solutions showed self-control.

CHAPTER 11

Color this medal once you have learned this word!

JOYFUL

I.   Say: Joyful: Joy' ful

II.   Meaning: To be happy, merry, and delighted

III.   Bible Verse: Psalm 47:1 "Clap your hands, all you nations; shout to God with cries of joy." (NIV)

IV.   Situation: Sometimes life has some sad things that happen. Whenever you can put a smile of joyfulness on your face it will lighten you up and may help a friend who is needing some joyfulness too!

V.   Solution: List some ways you can be joyful and happy.

1. *Grandma likes to give big hugs to share her joyfulness.*

2. I could help my parents feel more joyful by:

_____

3. I could help my friend get over a sad time by _____

_____ to help s/he become joyful again!

4. I could help myself keep joyful and bring happiness to others by:

_____

VI. ACTIVITY: **Being a Gym Teacher!**

Pick any or all of these games to have some fun! Allow a child to teach one!

Freeze Dance

1. One person plays some music.

2. When the music stops, everyone must freeze. If they move or fall over they are out. (Add times where those out can dance again!)

3. Repeat as often as the children desire.

Freeze Tag

1. One child is picked to be "IT" who tries to tag as many players as possible.

2. When a person is tagged they must freeze (stand still in place with one arm held out.)

3. If another free runner tags the frozen person's arm, they are melted   and can run around again.

4. The object of this game is to avoid being tagged.

5. To limit the area in which the children play, pool noodles can be used to mark the boundary limits.

6. A fun variation is to allow the person who is "IT" to use a pool noodle to tag people out!

Hide and Seek

1. Everyone hides while the "IT" person covers their eyes and counts slowly to fifty. "IT" then goes on a hunt to find everyone. The last person found wins and then becomes the next "IT".

2. For safety, limit the area in which the children hide.

CHAPTER 12

Color this medal once you have learned this word!

THOUGHTFUL

I.   Say: Thoughtful   Thot' ful

II.   Meaning: Thinking of other people's feeling and being kind to them.

III.   Bible Verse: Philippians 4:8 "... do whatever is true, whatever is noble, whatever is right, whatever is pure, whatever is lovely, whatever is admirable - if anything is excellence or praiseworthy - think about such things." (NIV)

IV.   Situation: Our actions speak louder than our words is an old saying. What actions of thoughtfulness could you show to people in these situations?

V.   Solution:

1. It is my Mother's birthday so I could:

_____

2. My best friend's family is moving to another State. I could:

_____

3. My neighbor is an elderly lady and she lives alone. I could:

_____

4. My brother is sad because his baseball team lost. I could:

_____

VI. ACTIVITY: **Being a Factory Owner!**

Making Greeting Cards

Today, we are going to pretend that we own a greeting card company. Think of two people you know who might be lonely, had something sad happen to them recently, or just need to have a special friend like you.

Directions:

#1 For each card you make, take one piece of paper and fold it in half once and then a second time so it becomes a card shaped like either of these two shapes:

#2 Draw a pretty picture on the front of the card and color it.

#3 Inside put the date, the person's name and write your note:

Put today's date here:

Dear _____, (Your friend's name)

Write you message in this space.

Your Friend,
Put your name here

#4 Ask a grown up to go with you to deliver it to your friend or they may want to put it in an envelope with a stamp on it and mail it!

CHAPTER 13

Color this medal once you have learned this word!

GOODNESS

I.   Say: Goodness   Good' ness

II.   Meaning: To be honest, upright, friendly, kind, and considerate to all.

III.   Bible Verse: Psalm 136:1 "Give thanks to the LORD, for He is good. His love endures forever." (NIV)

IV.   Situation: Today, each one of us needs to be good and to do good things to those in our family, our places of worship, our schools, and even to those who live in our neighborhoods or communities.

V.   Solution: Think of one idea that you could do to show your goodness to:

1. People in your Family: To show my goodness, I could:

_____

2. People in my place of worship: To show my goodness, I could:

_____

3. People in my school: To show my goodness, I could:

_____

4. People in my neighborhood: To show my goodness, I could:

_____

VI. ACTIVITY: **Being an Actor or Actress!**

Paper Bag Skits

Directions:

#1. Divide your group into teams of at least two children on each team.

#2. Give each team one small paper bag.

#3. Give the teams about 10 minutes to go around your home or classroom to find and put five odd things into their paper bag like: a spoon, a ball of yarn, a pair of sun glasses, a dog biscuit, and a hair brush. Each team should have a different collection of items in their bag.

#4. Gather the brown bags together and each team must pick one bag that is not their own bag.

#5. The teacher than will assign one specific place to each group out of this list: Home, place of worship, school, or neighborhood.

#6. Give each group about 10 minutes to make a skit up showing how they could model goodness in their _____ specific place.

#7. Each group must use every item in their bag in their skit including the paper bag!

#8. Have fun watching each other's skit! Goodness can be contagious!

CHAPTER 14

IMPARTIAL

Color this medal once you have learned this word!

IMPARTIAL

I.   Say: Impartial   Im par' shal

II. Meaning: Being fair, unbiased, equal…. Can mean disinterested

III. Bible Verse: Colossians 3:25 " Anyone who does wrong will be repaid for their wrongs, and there is no favoritism." (NIV)

IV. Situation: Many times, in life, people can like or dislike the same food, the same sport team, and even the same job! I have a friend who loves to cook but dislikes doing the dishes. I like to do both!

V.   Solution: Here is a picture of a cat dressed up! Is he well cared for, mistreated, or are you disinterested? How do you feel about this cat?

YOU DECIDE ?   FINAL ANSWER?

What I like about this picture of the cat is:

1. He looks silly.

2. _____Your idea?

What I do not like about this picture of the cat is:

1. He does not look happy and he may be hot?

2. _____ Your idea?

VI. ACTIVITY: **Being a Judge!**

We are going to pretend to be in a court today. Which job do you want?

Sign your name next to the job you want to do. If two of you want the same job, be impartial and flip a coin!

_____ Judge

_____ Member on the Jury

_____ Person or organization on trial

_____ Defense Lawyer
(defends person accused of crime
_____ Prosecuting Lawyer
(states crime against government

Procedures: Arrange chairs to look like a court room.

1. Court is called into order. **Judge** hits his desk with his pretend gavel.

2. **Jury members** are questioned & chosen. They cannot be a member of Doggy Kennel Club because **they would not be impartial**. (Why?)

3. **Prosecuting Lawyer** presents his case.
   This past Sundays, several members of the Doggy Kennel Club were found walking their unleased dogs on one of our town's public beaches. This is against the law. Dogs are not allowed to run freely on our beaches.

4. **Defense Lawyer:** Most of the Doggy Kennel Club members live in our high-rise apartment buildings and have no place to exercise their dogs. They should be able to use our beaches too.

5. With your parents help, run this trial. Was your trial fair, unbiased, or were many people just disinterested? Take a vote who won at the end of this trial.

CHAPTER 15

Color this medal once you have learned this word!

THANKFUL

I.   Say: Thankful   Thank' ful

II.   Meaning: To express appreciation, or gratitude, for a favor or gift

III.   Bible Verse: Psalm 106:1 "Praise the Lord. Give thanks to the Lord, for He is good; His love endures forever." (NIV)

IV.   Situation: There are many people and things to be thankful for in life.

V.   Solution: Grandma will list some of the things she is most thankful for on #1 and I invite you to add more ideas on the rest of this page.

1. *I am thankful for God, and my family; For my home, friends, food, clothing, and for my car and electricity too!*

2. _____ is thankful for: _____

3. _____ is thankful for: _____

4. _____ is thankful for: _____

ACTIVITY: **Being a Telephone Communicator!**

Directions:

1. Each person in your group is to pick one person they feel very thankful toward.
2. Write that person's name on the top line and then write all the things you appreciate that that person has done for you!
3. After we all have made our list, we will ask our parents if we can call that special person on the phone.
4. Call your special person and tell them about all the things that they do that make you feel so thankful to them. You will make them so happy!

Grandma's Special Person is : Cousin Ray	My Special Person is:	My Special Person is:
Because he is :	Because he is :	Because she is :
Kind		
Funny		
Smart		
Teaches me about photography		
Likes animals just like me !		

CHAPTER 16

Color this medal once you have learned this word!

FORGIVING

I.   Say: Forgiving: For   giv'   ing

II.   Meaning: To pardon, overlook, or excuse an offence or fault someone has done to you or others.

III.   Bible Verse: Ephesians 4:32   "Be kind and compassionate to one another, forgiving each other, just as in Christ God forgave you," (NIV)

IV.   Situation: Sometimes things that happen in life can hurt us. People can hurt us and we can hurt other people too. We can even hurt ourselves.

     God's Golden Rule says: "Treat others as we wish to be treated." When you do something wrong, do you want to be forgiven? Do likewise to others. Forgiving someone is a choice we each have.[3]

     Write down two good things that can happen to you when you forgive someone who has hurt you? Grandma has done the first one for you!

V.   Solution:

1. When I forgive, I feel peaceful and lose all angry feelings I had.

2. When I forgive, I _____.

3. When I forgive, I _____.

VI. ACTIVITY: **Being a Teacher!**

Let's Play: **Hot Potato!**

This is an interactive, encouraging game![4]

#1 If possible, go outside and bring a large plastic or soccer type ball.

#2 Have your group form a circle.

#3 Tell the children about a time when you forgave someone for hurting you.

#4 Roll or toss the ball to someone else in the circle and say " Hot Potato!"

#5 Now it is that person's time to share a time when they forgave someone.

#6 Give everyone a chance to share their story.

#7 When the ball gets back to you, ask different questions that are appropriate for the age level of the children or youth you are teaching. Some of your questions might be:

1. What is the meaning of forgiveness?

2. Have you ever had to say you were sorry to your Mom or Dad, to a teacher, to your brother or sister, or a dear friend? What did you do? What was their reaction?

3. How did you feel when you forgave someone?

4. How do you stop a person who is a bully? How do you forgive that person? Should you stay away from some people?

5. Does forgiving someone always mean automatic reconciliation?

    (Sometimes reconciliation takes time but it is good to try to forgive them.)

6. Did you ever get blamed for doing something you did not do? How do we and whom do we forgive when something like this happens?

CHAPTER 17

TRUSTWORTHY

Color this medal once you have learned this word!

TRUSTWORTHY

I.   Say: Trustworthy   Trust' wor thy

II.   Meaning: A person who is honest, always tells the truth and is reliable.

III.   Bible Verse: Zechariah 8:16 – 17   16 "These are the things you are to do: Speak the truth to each other, and render true and sound judgment in all your courts. 17 do not plot evil against each other, and do not love to swear falsely. I hate all this declares the LORD." (NIV)

IV.   Situation: Each person is to share with the group something that they did that showed they were trustworthy. After you share your story, check off in the chart below, some of the traits you used in your story.

Grandma's Story: My Mom gave me some money to buy a pumpkin at a road side stand. I picked out a pumpkin, paid the clerk. I brought my Mom back her change and a big pumpkin! She trusted me.

V.   Solution: My Trustworthy Chart[5]

I was:	
	Honest
	A good promise keeper
	A person who followed all the rules
	Kind
	Reliable
	Aware of what belonged to me and what did not.
	Good friend

VI. ACTIVITY: **Being a Trustworthy Guide!**

Today, each of us is going to take a friend on a blinded trust walk![6]

1. Divide into pairs.

2. Blindfold one child in each pair.

3. Each pair must hold hands.

4. The person who is not blind folded must guide their partner carefully through a path to a safe zone.

5. Adults can put a few obstacles like a chair in the pathway to make it more fun. Outside it could be a tree that needs to be walked around!

6. Once everyone is in the designated safe zone, switch the roles and put a new clean blind fold on the child who did not wear one before.

7. After everyone has had a chance to guide and be guided ask them how they felt about this experience. Was their guide a trustworthy friend?

8. Draw a picture here to show the blind walk you took with your friend.

CHAPTER 18

Color this medal once you have learned this word!

PEACEFUL

I.   Say: Peaceful: Pes' ful

II.   Meaning: Tranquil or freedom from quarrels, wars, or disagreements

III.   Bible Verse: Matthew 5:9 "Blessed are the peacemakers, for they will be called children of God." (NIV)

IV.   Situation: All of us can help **" keep the peace"** in our homes if we use soft voices and ask questions when we don't understand or don't agree with someone. In the chart below, put a check next to the statements that you think could help you **"keep the peace."**[7]

V.   Solution:

Check all Good Ideas	To **" keep the peace,"** I could say:
	1. I am sorry that you are upset.
	2. Would you like to know what I think?
	3. What did you mean by that?
	4. I need your help, could you please --------------------?
	5. Thank you for your opinion, I will think about it.

(All these ideas are good!)

VI. ACTIVITY: **Being Peace Ambassadors!**

Ssssshhhhh!
We are about to learn:

Grandma's Peaceful Silence Game[8]

We need: A place to be quiet!   .

             A timer

             A chime

             A flower or peace candle

We need to know: Know that one finger on lips means silence

                      Two fingers in air means peace.

                      Softly spoken " 25 Cent" Peaceful Words like:

                      Stillness

                      Calmness

                      Silence

                      Quiet

                      Relax

                      Serene

Introduce this Silence Game by softly saying something like: "Today, we are going to sit in a circle and slow down our bodies so they are very still. We are going to feel calm and relaxed. It will become so quiet in here that we will be able to hear sounds outside of our circle that we will share with each other later. Look at the flower (or candle) but no one can talk. Think of wonderful things that make you happy. It is nice to be quiet ....! The chime can start and end this fun time!"

CHAPTER 19

LOVING

Color this medal once you have learned this word!

LOVING

I.   Say: Loving   Lov' ing

II.   Meaning: To be caring, devoted, thoughtful, passionate, affectionate

III.   Bible Verse: John 3:16 "For God so loved the world that he gave his one and only Son, that whoever believes in him shall not perish but have eternal life." (NIV)

IV.   Situation: Grandma wants you to know that there are lots of ways we know when someone loves us. We love our family, our teachers, our friends, our pets, and even our home on earth. Love is a very good and happy feeling.

V.   Solution: Let's see what we each know and think about love.[9] Grandma filled in the first row for you. See if you can do the rest of the chart!

Ways I Know that I Am Loved are:	Make a list of People you love:	Ways I love and take care of my environment are:
1. People hug me!	1. My Dad	1. Plant a tree or flowers
2.	2.	2.
3.	3.	3.
4.	4.	4.

VI. ACTIVITY: **Being a Book Publisher!**[10]

Today, we are going to draw the first four pages in our own family's picture book. If you have more than four people and pets in your family than ask for another piece of paper. Remember to print the name of each person in your family under their picture.

The _____Family Album

Name:	Name:
Name:	Name:

CHAPTER 20

FAITHFUL

Color this medal once you have learned this word!

FAITHFUL

I.   Say: Faithful: Faith' ful

II. Meaning: Being dependable, trustworthy, and loyal in relationship
                  with God and other people.[11]

III. Bible Verse: Proverbs 3:3   Let love and faithfulness never leave you;
                  bind them around your neck, write them on the tablet of
                  your heart." (NIV)

IV. Situation: Grandma wants you to know that anything you want to be is
                shown by what you do![12]

     If you want to be kind, …… do kind things.
     If you want to be loving, …... show love in action.
     If you want to be full of faith, …… show your faith in action.

     How can I show faithfulness to God with my actions?

V.   Solution: Grandma thinks attending church and praying are some ways.
               Write some ideas you have to show your faith in action:

     1.

     2.

     3.

VI. ACTIVITY: **Being Jewelers!**

Since our Bible verse on faithfulness tells us "to bind love and faithfulness around our neck," we are going to make a necklace today.[13] We may make it out of colorful beads, or macaroni, or we just may draw what we look like with a colorful necklace of beads around our necks!

As we are busy stringing our beads or drawing a picture of ourselves wearing a cool looking necklace, let's share with one another stories about when God has been faithful to us.

Grandma will share one of her stories of God's faithfulness first.

One day I went fishing with my family of four but we only owned three fishing poles. All of us loved to fish. I decided to take a book to read when I couldn't fish. I prayed to God that I would be a good sport during the times I couldn't fish. Guess what happened?

The very first cast that Dad took snagged a branch. He pulled and pulled but a branch did not come up out of the water but a good fishing pole did! The hook on Dad's pole had caught a fishing pole someone had lost in the water! We asked around the dock area to see if it belonged to anyone but no one claimed it. Dad gave the pole to me!

God is so wonderful as we all got to fish that day!

Now, it is your turn to share your faith stories about God with each other!

THE LORD'S PRAYER

Our Father, who art in heaven,
Hallowed be Thy name.
Thy kingdom come.
Thy will be done on earth as it is in heaven.
Give us this day our daily bread.
And forgive us our debts,
As we also have forgiven our debtors.
And do not lead us into temptation,
But deliver us from evil.
For Thine is the kingdom, and the power,
And the glory, forever.

Amen.

(Matthew 6:9–15)
(NASB)

CONCLUSION

BE

GOOD!

END NOTES

1. www.genius.com/Leegreenwood-pledge-of-allegiance

2. https://brightfutures-counseling.com 5 Strategies for Teaching Self Control To Kids (15 July 2029)

3. www.mindful,healthymind,healthylife.com Maryam Abdullah: How to Teach Kids Forgiveness Skills (1April 2019

4. Ourpastimes.com/childrens-games-demonstrate-forgiveness

5. www.teachkidshow/teach-your-child-to-be-trustworthy

6. www.momjunction.com/article/trust-building-activities-for-kids Bebolina Raja (3July2020)

7. www.realsimple.com Ways to Keep Peace

8. www.CarrotsAreOrange.com Silence Game

9. www.momentsaday.com / activities-to-teach-children-about-love

10. Ibid.

11. www.Thelittlesandme.com The Fruits of the Spirit is Faithfulness Kids Activities (20July2018)

12. www.rootedfamily.com Rachel Wojo: What Does It Mean to be Faithful (29March2017)

13. www.Thelittleonesandme.com The Fruits of the spirit is Faithfulness (29March2017)

ABOUT THE AUTHOR

Judith M. Alford received both a Bachelor of Science (1969) and a Master of Science in Child Development (1972) degrees from the University of Georgia in Athens, Georgia. In 1972 - 1973 in Athens, Georgia, she worked with the Clarke County Board of Education under a Title 4A project. Her task was to help write the State of Georgia's first kindergarten curriculum with three other authors.

In the mid-1970s, she moved to New Castle, PA where she raised two sons. She directed Girl Scout Camps in Western PA during the summers and family camping experiences in the fall and winters.

From 1985 – 1998 she taught first grade and fifth grade science at Laurel Elementary School in New Castle, PA. In the summers she taught High School students computer classes to help them achieve better scores on their SAT exams.

While living in Western Pennsylvania, she served the United Methodist Church in several short-term mission trips to Germany and Russia. On one trip she served as the lay leader that took nineteen Methodist youth to Germany for three weeks. In 1998 – 1999, she traveled across the United States in and RV with her husband

Jim. They did mission work that year for the Methodist Nomads working with the homeless in Phoenix, Arizona, and at Rust State College in Holly Springs, Mississippi.

In 1999, the couple moved to South Carolina, where Judy received a call from God for preaching at the age of fifty-two! She earned a Master of Divinity (2004) from Erskine Theological Seminary in Due West, SC. As an ordained elder in the South Carolina Conference of the United Methodist Church, she and her husband served six churches. (2002 – 2014) It was during this time that she wrote Bible Studies for all four years of Bishop Richard Wilke's Disciple Bible Studies. Her lessons were copyrighted by Cokesbury, the United Methodist Publishing House.

Judy retired in 2014 to care for her terminally ill husband who died in 2015.

In 2020 Judy wrote and had published her first book: *The Hands of God A Collection of Short Stories about God's Intervention in Human Lives.* Today, she lives in Greenwood, SC where she enjoys writing, making stained glass windows, and serving the LORD, the delight of her life.